Coming Soon ...

My Life: Who Decides? by Dr William Molloy

An in-depth look at the issues – practical, ethical, social and political – surrounding an individual's right to decide when, where and how to die.

Who makes these difficult decisions now? Who should be making them in future? *My Life: Who Decides?* provides informative answers to these and other crucial questions of our time.

A Penguin Book scheduled for Fall 1992 release

Let Me Decide

The Health Care Directive That Speaks for You When You Can't

Dr William Molloy MB, FRCP(C)
and
Virginia Mepham

PENGUIN BOOKS
Published by the Penguin Group
Penguin Books Canada Ltd, 10 Alcorn Avenue, Toronto,
Ontario, Canada M4V 3B2
Penguin Books Ltd, 27 Wrights Lane, London W8 5TZ,
England
Viking Penguin, a division of Penguin Books USA Inc.,
375 Hudson Street, New York, New York 10014, USA
Penguin Books Australia Ltd, Ringwood, Victoria, Australia
Penguin Books (NZ) Ltd, 182-190 Wairau Road,
Auckland 10, New Zealand
Penguin Books Ltd, Registered Offices:
Harmondsworth, Middlesex, England

First published 1989
Published in Penguin Books, 1992

1 3 5 7 9 10 8 6 4 2

Copyright © Dr D.W. Molloy, 1989

Canadian Cataloguing in Publication Data
Molloy, William, 1953-
Let me decide
Rev. and expanded ed. of: Let me decide.
ISBN 0-14-017267-X
1. Terminally ill – Medical care.   2. Terminally ill – Legal status, laws, etc.   3. Patient advocacy.
I. Mepham, Virginia, 1910- . II. Title.
R726.M65 1992   344'.04197   C92-093486-2

Printed and bound in Canada

For information on bulk purchases of this booklet,
please contact Mr Nolan Machan, Special Sales Department,
Penguin Books Canada Limited, 10 Alcorn Avenue #300,
Toronto, Ontario, M4V 3B2 Tel: (416) 925-2249 Fax: (416) 925-0068

This book is
dedicated to
DEBORAH and TED

Just as I choose a ship to sail in
or a house to live in,
so I choose a death for my passage
from this life.

SENECA (4BC-45AD)

Contents

Dr William Molloy
MB, BCh, BAO, MRCP(I), FRCP(C)

Willie was born in Waterford, Ireland, and qualified in medicine at University College Cork in 1977. He came to Canada in 1981 and trained in geriatrics at the University of Manitoba, University of Western Ontario and McMaster University.

A consultant geriatrician, he is currently Director of the Memory Clinic and Director of the Geriatric Research Group at the Hamilton Civic Hospitals. He is also Assistant Professor of Medicine and Director of Research in the Division of Geriatric Medicine at McMaster University. Dr Molloy strongly advocates increasing patients' rights in health care.

He is married to Deborah and has two sons, James and Alexander.

Virginia Mepham
RN

Virginia graduated in 1932 from the Hamilton General Hospital School of Nursing. She is a founding member of The Planned Parenthood Federation of Canada and served as president of the Hamilton chapter for 6 years.

Mrs Mepham has spent much of her life working as a volunteer toward improving the lives of women, and has worked with Dr Molloy in the development of this Directive since 1989.

She was married to Dr Ted Mepham, a Hamilton physician, for 56 years and became a widow in 1988.

Acknowledgements

The authors would like to thank Patricia Black, Jack Kelly and Gerry Elphick for their generous contributions to this booklet. We would also like to acknowledge the assistance of the Healthy Choices for Seniors Committee in Hamilton and the Clinical Ethics Committee at McMaster University for their assistance in the development of the Directive.

For their support and encouragement, thanks to the many medical doctors who provided input: Stuart MacLeod, Stephen Levenson, John Phin, Alwyn Cunje, Efrem Alemayehu, Jack Hirsh, Arnold Johnson, John Thomas, Warren Davidson, Roger Clarnette, Sheilah Lamb, Martin Eisemann; and to Rosalie Capretta, Kevin Smith, Kay McPhee, Judy Lever, Linda Rees, Janet Flett, Tim Standish, John Horsman, Judy Kent, Mafalda Urbanyi, Barbara Toohey, Gail Butt and Paul Milne.

Thanks are also owed to many organizations for their enthusiastic support: Ancaster Information Centre; Ancaster Senior Achievement Centre; Alzheimer Societies of Halton-Wentworth, and Guelph and District; Chedoke McMaster Hospitals; Death With Dignity; Division of Geriatric Medicine,

McMaster University; Educational Centre for Aging and Health, McMaster University; Geriatric Research Group; Gray Panthers; Hamilton Civic Hospitals; Hamilton Memorial Society; Idlewyld Manor; Manitoba Law Reform Commission; McMaster University Faculty of Health Sciences; Older Adult Centres' Association of Ontario; Ontario Medical Association; Ryerson United Church; Simpson, Wigle, Barristers and Solicitors; Social Services Department of Hamilton-Wentworth; St. Peter's Seminary; St. Joseph's Hospital; and St. Joseph's Villa.

Special thanks to Gord Guyatt, Roberta Labelle, Alba Mitchell and Norman Flett for their collaboration, to Cynthia Good, Jackie Kaiser, John Meyers and everyone at Penguin, and to Karen Mead for her continued support and assistance during the development of this booklet. Finally, sincere thanks to the Seniors Independence Programme, Health and Welfare Canada; CIBA GEIGY Canada; Ontario Ministry of Health, Research Division; and Physicians' Services Incorporated. Without the generous funding assistance provided by these organizations, this booklet would not have been possible.

Introduction

The purpose of this booklet is to give you the means to record your wishes for your own health care. If you should become incapacitated by disease or injury and cannot communicate for yourself at some time in the future, the "Let Me Decide" Health Care Directive will speak for you.

Over the last fifty years medicine has advanced at an amazing pace. What would have been considered miraculous fifty years ago is now routine. People are kept alive with heart, kidney and liver transplants. Arms are sewn back on, and cancers that were once fatal are cured. At the same time modern medicine has become more complicated, more technological and more sophisticated.

The general public can be overwhelmed by the amount of technology in modern health care. Many people are also confused by the jargon that health professionals use. A person can go into hospital and have an ECG, EEG, EMG, colonoscopy, laparoscopy, bronchoscopy, or a hundred other tests for diseases such as SLE, COPD, or IHD. For the person with the disease this jargon is meaningless. The patient experiences pain, shortness of breath, weight loss or tiredness. Blood tests and x-rays mean needles and scans that create endless printouts and images on screens.

At the same time, the general public has become better informed, as newspapers, magazines, television and movies educate us about illnesses and potential treatments. Groups such as the Alzheimer Society, Cystic Fibrosis Foundation, Cancer Society and Kidney Foundation also provide information and support for patients and families. This combination of high technology and better-informed patients can lead to conflict between patients and the health care team. Patients and their families want to keep control over their own bodies. At the same time, they may feel helpless in the face of modern technology. Modern hospitals are medical-industrial complexes that can take over and bewilder the patients.

Medical staff face a similar dilemma. Doctors don't want to make difficult decisions that will affect the rest of a patient's life. But without guidance from the patients, doctors must do everything to preserve life. Doctors and nurses are employed by institutions and can be forced to follow their rules.

The freedom to decide one's own destiny is the right of every competent person. This includes the right to accept or refuse specific medical treatment. Many have definite opinions on how they would wish to be treated. People want to choose their own health care. They want to have control over their way of life and manner of death.

Seriously ill people are often not able to make decisions. For example, people with pneumonia or a stroke may be too confused to make choices. They may not be able to make their wishes known. Many are concerned that in the event of a serious illness they may not receive the treatment that they would want. They are worried that they may be too sick to let doctors know their wishes, or that they may not even be asked. Some fear that they will be connected to machines and kept alive too long.

When we are too ill to make decisions, family, friends or doctors must make them for us.

These decisions are often very difficult and may present a "no-win" situation for the family.

When the family asks doctors to do "everything possible" to keep a loved one alive and that person dies in a few weeks or months, the family may feel guilty that they put the patient through needless tests and treatments. They may feel that all they had done was prolong the patient's suffering and postpone death.

On the other hand, if they let their family member "die with dignity" without treatment, they may feel they should have done more.

Another problem develops if the family cannot agree on the best treatment. Some may want everything done to keep the person alive. Others may want only palliative care — that is, care that provides comfort and relief from pain, but does not aim to cure the condition.

Children from divorced marriages may resent step-parents or common-law spouses making decisions for their parents. Children who have not been in contact for years may turn up when their parents are dying and involve themselves in the decisions. They may not know their parent's wishes. These children may demand that doctors do everything possible to bring their parents back, so they can have time to make peace with them. Friends and other family members who have stayed in close contact may accept the parent's death more easily, and may request palliative care.

Family conflicts and disagreements can cause lasting bitterness. How can we protect ourselves to make sure we get the health care we want? How can we let others know our wishes? How can we protect our families and friends from this dilemma?

When we discuss these concerns in advance, we can prevent conflict later among those who are forced to act on these decisions. If we have clearly stated our wishes, then doctors and family don't have to guess what kind of treatment we would have asked for. It prevents potential conflict and guilt in the family. It removes the need for "second-guessing" — that is, trying to guess what we would want.

The drawback of informal discussions about these matters is that family and friends may not recall them accurately in a time of crisis, perhaps years later. By documenting our wishes in writing, we can prevent this problem, and give clear instructions for our health care in the future. This way, if the time comes when we are too sick to decide for ourselves, our doctors, families and friends will know our wishes. And we can receive the treatment we want.

What Is an Advance Directive?

An advance directive is any written statement that expresses a person's wishes in advance.

The commonest form of advance directive, the one we are most familiar with, is the *will.* A will is an advance directive containing specific instructions — directives — about our possessions. We use wills to tell others what we want done with our possessions after our death.

A slightly different kind of advance directive is a *power of attorney.* This directive may not give specific instructions; instead, it empowers another person to act on our behalf should we ever be unable to make decisions ourselves.

A third kind of advance directive deals specifically with health care. It contains instructions about our care in case we are not able to make health care decisions for ourselves at a later date. The "Let Me Decide" Health Care Directive enables us to let others know our wishes about medical treatment.

For example, we could at some future time be incapacitated by a stroke or a serious head injury. These illnesses affect our ability to think, reason and speak. The health care directive allows us to give instructions *in advance.*

As long as we remain competent, able to consider and communicate health care choices, we must make these decisions for ourselves. An advance directive is designed to be used only if we are unable to make our wishes known.

There are two types of advance directives: "instructional" and "proxy."

An *instructional directive* states which treatments are wanted or not wanted under any given circumstance. These statements can be as general or specific as desired. But the more specific they are, the easier they are for family and doctors to follow.

Do not think of an instructional directive as limited to treatment of terminal or irreversible conditions — it can also apply to curable, reversible conditions.

A *proxy directive* nominates another person (the proxy or advocate) to make decisions for your health care if you become incompetent. This advocate will have the ability to make health care decisions in much the same way as a power of attorney does for financial matters.

The "Let Me Decide" Health Care Directive combines both an instructional and a proxy directive. This helps ensure that your wishes are followed. For example, written instructions may not be specific enough to guide a doctor in all situations. And if the advocate or proxy is unavailable during a crisis, written instructions will enable the doctor to proceed according to your wishes.

3

The "Let Me Decide" Directive: An Overview

The "Let Me Decide" Directive has been developed not just for senior citizens or the terminally ill, but for adults of all ages. It can be used by everybody to plan their future health care.

The Directive uses some medical terms so that doctors can interpret it effectively. This means that if you want to use the "Let Me Decide" Directive, you must first understand the medical terms used. To help you, a glossary is included at the back of this booklet. For more information, please consult your family doctor.

The Directive deals with a variety of treatment options depending on whether your condition is reversible or irreversible. These include your wishes for medical treatment in the event of life-threatening illness, inability to feed yourself, and cardiac arrest.

Let's take a look now at what we mean by "reversible" and "irreversible." We'll consider life-threatening illnesses, feeding, and cardiac arrest in later chapters.

IRREVERSIBLE CONDITION

When your condition is irreversible there is no possibility of a complete recovery. Illnesses such as Alzheimer's disease, Parkinson's disease, certain cancers, strokes and AIDS are examples of irreversible illnesses that may lead to permanent disability.

People react differently to permanent disability. Some people would not consider themselves disabled if they were confined to a wheelchair or even bedridden. Others would consider this an unacceptable loss of independence.

For instance, if Beethoven had gone blind instead of deaf, he still could have heard his music and composed. Blindness would have made little difference to him. But a painter such as Picasso would dread blindness much more than deafness. So the same disabilities can affect people in different ways.

Since each person would accept different irreversible disabilities, it is important to know in advance what each person would or would not be prepared to accept. Otherwise families and doctors may have to guess what a person would want.

Before you fill out the "Let Me Decide" Directive, you need to think about what level of irreversible disability you would tolerate in your life. It is often difficult to know this in advance. Each of us must consider this question carefully and discuss it with our family and doctor.

Diseases such as cancer, multiple sclerosis, stroke, Parkinson's or Alzheimer's may affect one's ability to think and function independently. So don't think in terms of specific illnesses. Think about everyday activities such as walking, dressing, talking and eating. Then describe what you would not be prepared to accept when you define "irreversible condition" in your Personal Statement.

For instance, don't say "I would consider Alzheimer's to be an irreversible condition." Many people with a mild form of Alzheimer's disease live independent lives, drive cars and experience only minor problems.

It is much clearer to say, "If the time ever

comes when I am unable to dress myself, or to recognize my family, or if I lose control over my bladder or bowel and there is no hope of recovery then I would consider that to be an irreversible condition." In this way all the illnesses and injuries that can cause a specific condition are covered in your Directive.

REVERSIBLE CONDITION

A reversible condition is one that can be cured completely with treatment. A bleeding ulcer is a common reversible condition. Infections such as acute bronchitis or pneumonia usually respond to treatment and can be cured when they occur in healthy individuals, and they leave no permanent disability. However, when they occur in people already weakened by chronic diseases, they can often be fatal.

Your instructions for treating reversible conditions may permit the use of technologies that you would consider unacceptable in an irreversible state. For example, you might want antibiotics for a severe case of pneumonia if you were fit and healthy. You might reject antibiotics if you had pneumonia and terminal cancer.

You have the right to decide which conditions you consider to be reversible and irreversible, and what level of care you would want in each case.

The "Let Me Decide" Personal Health Care Directive has 4 pages; let us review the purpose of the different sections now.

I. Introduction
This section states the reasons why you have completed this Directive. It advises physicians that the Directive should not be used if you are conscious and able to make decisions. It should only be used if you are incapacitated by disease or injury and unable to make decisions for yourself.

II. Advocate(s) and Family Doctor
In this section you identify your family doctor and your advocate(s) with names, addresses and telephone numbers. If possible, both home and work numbers should be given, along with additional numbers where these people may be reached in an emergency.

III. Personal Health Care Chart
This chart gives your wishes for treatment in the event of a life-threatening illness, inability to feed yourself, and cardiac arrest, depending on whether your condition is reversible or irreversible.

We recommend that you review your instructions in the chart from time to time. Space is provided for this updated information.

IV. Definitions

This section contains a brief explanation of terms used in the Directive, so that medical staff will clearly understand your instructions.

V. Personal Statement

This section contains your personal statement about any particular area of health care that is not covered in the other parts of the Directive.

It has an introductory statement ("I consider an irreversible condition to be any condition . . .") which you are encouraged to complete in your own words, so that others will know what level of irreversible disability you would consider unacceptable. Most people would want different care for a reversible and irreversible illnesses, so it is important for you to state your wishes as clearly as possible.

There is a section where you can make your wishes known about organ donation, blood transfusion, post mortem and cremation.

Important Note

When choosing any level of care, it is important to keep in mind that you may not necessarily receive the level of care you request. For example, if you asked for "intensive care" for a life-threatening illness, you would not automatically be admitted to intensive care for every single illness. If admitted to hospital with a treatable bleeding ulcer, for example, you would not necessarily require intensive care.

On the other hand, if you requested "palliative care" for an illness, you might go to the intensive care unit. For example, if you developed chest pain from a heart attack that could not be controlled at home or in an ordinary hospital ward, then you might be transferred to intensive care because the staff there were the best equipped to provide palliative care — that is, to treat the pain and keep you comfortable.

Life-Threatening Illness

The "Let Me Decide" Health Care Directive enables you to state what level of care you would like to receive in the event of life-threatening illness. You may specify that you would like one level of care if your condition is reversible, and another level of care if your condition is irreversible.

A life-threatening illness is any illness that can cause death. Pneumonia, for example, is a life-threatening illness.

Although pneumonia can be fatal, most healthy people recover fully from it. A healthy child or adult who develops pneumonia would want to be vigorously treated. But a person who is already dying from an incurable illness and is suffering pain may wish to allow the illness to run its course with no more than palliative care.

People rarely die directly from chronic illnesses such as Parkinson's disease, Alzheimer's or cancer. Instead they die from complications arising from these diseases. The complications that usually cause death are pneumonia or blood clots to the lungs (known as pulmonary embolism). In many cases, patients with these chronic illnesses may be so weak that they have no resistance to fight infections such as pneumonia.

If a decision is made to treat an acute life-threatening illness in a dying patient, more tests and investigations are usually required (for example, needles, x-rays, intravenous lines or surgery). These procedures can be uncomfortable and/or painful for the patient.

Doctors may advise families at such times to allow the person to die peacefully, so that the patient will not suffer any further. Palliative care merely aims to keep the person comfortable and relieve pain. With this approach, treatment is not aimed at cure, but at maintaining comfort.

For this reason, pneumonia has sometimes been called the "old man's friend." It often allows a dying person to die peacefully without a great deal of suffering.

You should be familiar with the four levels of care described in this section: palliative, limited, surgical, and intensive.

PALLIATIVE CARE

At this level, tests and treatments are done not to prolong life but to maintain comfort. The aim of treatment is to keep the patient warm, dry and free of pain.

Patients who have requested this level of care might have surgery, if that could improve their comfort or relieve pain. For example, if you broke a hip and had requested palliative care, surgery could be performed to pin the hip, if this was the most effective way to relieve the pain.

Similarly, antibiotics might be prescribed, not to cure an infection, but because they might improve your comfort.

If you requested palliative care and had bleeding in the stomach or intestine, you would not receive blood transfusions or drugs to stop the bleeding. If you were at home, you would not be transferred to hospital for tests or treatments. You would be moved to hospital only if you could not be kept comfortable at home.

This section contains your
Personal Health Care Directive

———————

Please detach centre staple and
remove inner pages before
completing your Directive

Basic Feeding: Spoon feed with regular diet. Give all fluids by mouth that can be tolerated, but make no attempt to feed by special diets, intravenous fluids or tubes.

Supplemental Feeding: Give supplements or special diets, for example, high calorie, fat or protein supplements.

Intravenous Feeding: Give nutrients (water, salt, carbohydrate, protein and fat) by intravenous infusions.

Tube Feeding: Use tube feeding. There are two main types:
   1. **Nasogastric Tube:** a soft plastic tube passed through the nose or mouth into the stomach.
   2. **Gastrostomy Tube:** a soft plastic tube passed directly into stomach through the skin over the abdomen.

No CPR: Make no attempt to resuscitate.

CPR: Use cardiac massage with mouth-to-mouth breathing; may also include intravenous lines, electric shocks to the heart (defibrillators), tubes in throat to lungs (endotrachial tubes).

Palliative Care

- keep me warm, dry, and pain free
- do not transfer to hospital unless absolutely necessary
- only give measures that enhance comfort or minimize pain; e.g., morphine for pain
- intravenous line started only if it improves comfort; e.g., for hydration
- no x-rays, blood tests or antibiotics unless they are given to improve comfort

Limited Care (includes Palliative)

- may or may not transfer to hospital
- intravenous therapy may be appropriate
- antibiotics should be used sparingly
- a trial of appropriate drugs may be used
- no invasive procedures; e.g., surgery
- do not transfer to Intensive Care Unit

III. PERSONAL HEALTH CARE CHART

This chart is to be consulted only if I am no longer able to make or communicate my own decisions.

My choices are noted in the spaces provided below each section.

In the event of Life-Threatening Illness, please provide the following care:		In the event I am not able to feed myself, please provide the following care:		In the event of Cardiac Arrest, please provide the following care:	
If my condition is: REVERSIBLE →	IRREVERSIBLE →	If my condition is: REVERSIBLE →	IRREVERSIBLE →	If my condition is: REVERSIBLE →	IRREVERSIBLE →
Palliative Limited Surgical Intensive	Palliative Limited Surgical Intensive	Basic Supplemental Intravenous Tube	Basic Supplemental Intravenous Tube	No CPR CPR	No CPR CPR

Write your choice here

Date and initial

Date: Patient: Advocate #1:   Advocate #2:   Physician:

PERSONAL HEALTH CARE DIRECTIVE

I. INTRODUCTION

In this Directive I have stated my wishes for my own health care should the time ever come when I am not able to communicate because of illness or injury. This Directive should never be used if I am able to decide for myself. It must never be substituted for my judgment if I am competent to make these decisions.

If the time comes when I am unable to make these decisions, I would like this Directive to be followed and respected. In an emergency, please contact my advocate(s) or my family doctor, listed below. If these people are not available, then please do as I have requested in this Directive. Thank you.

I have thought about and discussed my decision with my family, friends and my family doctor. I do not want to leave these decisions to my family, my doctor or strangers who do not know me.

Dated this ____ **day of** _____, 19 ____ .

SIGNED: _____   _____
Signature   Print Name

_____
Health Insurance Number

II. ADVOCATE(S) and FAMILY PHYSICIAN

Advocate #1

_____   _____
Name   Address

_____   _____
Home Tel. #   Office Tel. #

Advocate #2

_____   _____
Name   Address

_____   _____
Home Tel. #   Office Tel. #

Advocate #3

_____   _____
Name   Address

_____   _____
Home Tel. #   Office Tel. #

This document should be reviewed once a year, after an illness, or if there is any change in health.

You can use the space below to show any changes in your Directive.

Write your choice here				
Date and initial here	*Patient:*	*Advocate #1:*	*Advocate #2:*	*Physician:*
Write your choice here				
Date and initial here	*Patient:*	*Advocate #1:*	*Advocate #2:*	*Physician:*

IV. DEFINITIONS OF TERMS USED IN THE DIRECTIVE

Reversible Condition: Condition that may be cured without any remaining disability; e.g., multiple sclerosis, stroke, severe head injury, Alzheimer's disease.

Irreversible Condition: Condition that will leave lasting disabilities; e.g., multiple sclerosis, stroke, severe head injury, Alzheimer's disease.

Surgical Care (includes Limited)

- transfer to acute care hospital (where patient may be evaluated)
- emergency surgery if necessary
- do not admit to Intensive Care Unit
- do not ventilate (except during and after surgery); i.e., tube down throat and connected with machine

Intensive Care (includes Surgical)

- transfer to acute-care hospital without hesitation
- admit to Intensive Care Unit if necessary
- ventilate if necessary
- insert central line; i.e., main arteries for fluids when other veins collapse
- provide surgery, biopsies, all life-support systems and transplant surgery
- do everything possible to maintain life

V. Personal Statement

I consider an irreversible condition to be any condition _____

_____

_____

_____

_____

I agree to the following procedures: (write Yes or No)

POST MORTEM _____   BLOOD TRANSFUSION _____

ORGAN DONATION _____   CREMATION _____

This section contains your
Personal Health Care Directive

———————————

Please detach centre staple and
remove inner pages before
completing your Directive

LIMITED CARE

This level includes treatment that is more extensive than "palliative," but less than "surgical." For example, if you requested limited care and developed pneumonia, you would receive antibiotics. You could have blood tests, intravenous fluids, x-rays and oxygen. If you had bleeding from the stomach or intestine, you could receive blood transfusions or drugs.

If you were at home when you became ill, you would be transferred to hospital only if proper care could not be given in the home. You would not receive emergency surgery to stop the bleeding. You would not receive any medical tests that required a general anesthetic, and would not be put on life-support machines. You would not go on a kidney machine (for dialysis) if your kidneys failed.

SURGICAL CARE

At this level you would receive blood tests, x-rays, surgery and would be considered for a kidney machine. You would not be put on a breathing machine (a ventilator) unless it was needed during or after surgery. Sometimes patients need ventilators after surgery until they are able to breathe on their own again.

At surgical care, you would receive intravenous fluids and blood transfusions if you had a life-threatening bleed from the bowel. A tube might be passed into the stomach or lower bowel (an endoscopy) to find the cause of bleeding. If necessary, doctors would perform surgery to correct the bleeding.

You would not be transferred to intensive care, unless that was the best place to keep you comfortable. You would not be put on a breathing machine unless you were under anesthetic during surgery.

You would be transferred from home to hospital without hesitation if necessary.

INTENSIVE CARE

At this level, everything a modern hospital has to offer would be used to maintain life. If you requested this level of care you would receive surgery, biopsies, all life-support systems (kidney machines, breathing machines) and transplant surgery if possible (including heart, kidney, liver or bone marrow transplants).

If you were at home, you would be transferred to hospital. If you were in a small community hospital, you would be transferred to a larger hospital, with a larger range of facilities, if this were beneficial.

Feeding

Many people with severe illnesses are not able to feed themselves. If they are unconscious and can't swallow or communicate, they may be given fluids or food artificially to keep them alive. Someone must decide how they will be fed.

The "Let Me Decide" Directive enables you to choose what kind of feeding support you would want if you were not able to feed yourself and unable to let others know your wishes. There are four options to feed those who are not able to eat a normal diet: basic, supplemental, intravenous and tube.

BASIC FEEDING

At this level of care you would be spoon fed with a regular diet (fluid and solids). You would receive fluids, if you were uncomfortable from thirst. This might include using an intravenous line to prevent dehydration. But the amount of fluid given for this purpose is much smaller than if you were being fed through an intravenous line. In this case, fluids are being given for comfort only.

SUPPLEMENTAL FEEDING
(includes basic feeding)

At this level, supplements are given in addition to the basic diet. For instance, you may be able to swallow solids, but not liquids, or vice versa. You may not be able to eat a regular diet and may be given high energy supplements or extra vitamins. This level includes basic level care, but does not include tubes or intravenous feeding.

INTRAVENOUS FEEDING
(includes supplemental feeding)

At this level, fluids and food can be given directly into the veins. This method only works for a limited time because the intravenous fluids and the needles usually damage the veins. Eventually none of the veins in the arms can be used any longer. When this happens, larger veins nearer the heart, in the chest and neck, must be used. Using these larger veins, it is possible to give more food and fluids directly into the circulation. This method of feeding is called "total parenteral nutrition."

Intravenous feeding is used for people whose stomachs or intestines don't work properly. If your intestine is not absorbing food, then there is no point in using special diets or other means of getting nutrients to the stomach; only intravenous feeding can sustain life.

Intravenous feeding requires no surgery. In some cases, minor procedures are used to insert these lines into the large veins near the heart.

TUBE FEEDING
(includes intravenous feeding)

If you request tube feeding, then you may receive nasogastric and/or gastrostomy tubes in the event you can no longer feed yourself.

Nasogastric tubes are soft plastic tubes passed through the nose into the stomach. They are used when you can still digest food but cannot swallow. Some people find these tubes uncomfortable or painful and pull them out time and time again. Others tolerate them well.

Once these tubes are in place, minced-up food and liquids can be passed through to the stomach. In this way it is possible to give enough food and liquids to sustain you almost indefinitely. However, nasogastric tubes are not suitable for prolonged periods. If they are pulled up into the throat, even accidentally, food can be passed directly into the lungs, which may be fatal.

Gastrostomy tubes are passed through the skin over the abdomen, directly into the stomach. This method of feeding is used when you can't swallow or can't tolerate a nasogastric tube. When a person needs feeding for a long time, this method is preferable to a nasogastric tube.

Gastrostomy tubes can be surgically installed without a general anesthetic. Once they are in place, they are fairly painless and trouble-free. People can even have baths and showers with them. They can be used to give people enough food and fluids to sustain them indefinitely.

6

CPR

Cardio-pulmonary resuscitation, or CPR, is an emergency procedure that attempts to restore breathing and heartbeat in a person whose heart or breathing, or both, have stopped. Because it is a crisis when the heart or breathing stops, decisions about CPR should be made as far in advance as possible.

CPR includes external cardiac massage (pumping on the chest to keep the blood flowing through the heart) and mouth-to-mouth breathing. It may also include drugs, electric defibrillators (machines to shock the heart into action) or a breathing machine (mechanical ventilation).

CPR was originally developed to help those whose hearts had stopped from a heart attack or drowning. If a healthy person's heart stops, that person has had a cardiac arrest, and there is a good chance of reviving the individual and returning him or her to normal life. CPR can give a person many extra years of living.

In chronically ill older adults, CPR is nearly always unsuccessful. Those few who do survive often do not live very long. But in hospitals today, the medical staff are required to do everything possible to save a person's life in an emergency. Unless specific instructions are given to the contrary, every patient is given CPR.

The "No CPR" order states that no attempt should be made to revive a person whose breathing or heart has stopped. Such orders are becoming more common. Many people fear the use of medical technology to prolong life artificially, and are asserting their wishes for a peaceful end.

Few of us consider these decisions prior to an emergency. But people's wishes must be known so that those who want aggressive treatment can receive it, and those who don't will not be subjected to it. Unless there is a doctor's written order that a patient does not want CPR or other life-saving treatments, the patient will receive them, because hospital staff are obliged to take every step to save a life.

This Directive enables you to decide in advance about CPR, and record your wishes in the Personal Health Care Chart.

The Personal Statement

This part of the "Let Me Decide" Health Care Directive must be considered very carefully. The more exact you can be, the easier it will be for others to follow your wishes. Discuss this thoroughly with your advocates.

The personal statement should define what irreversible condition you would consider intolerable. This is the irreversible condition so severe that you would probably want only palliative care. In this condition, you would probably not want aggressive care that would prolong life at all costs.

This is a very important statement to make, because people have different ideas about what disabilities and medical treatments would be intolerable to them. Some people would be terrified at the thought of quadriplegia. Others might fear being unable to feed themselves or losing bowel or bladder control. Some would never want to live in an institution and others would never want to be tube fed.

It is important to state as clearly as possible what *you* would and would not accept.

When you describe what you would consider an irreversible condition, do not say, "Alzheimer's disease or cancer." Don't name diseases, because there are great variations in the conditions that these diseases cause. Instead, describe what you consider irreversible in terms of everyday living. It is clearer to say: "If the time should ever come when I am unable to wash, dress or feed myself or, if I can't speak to my family or make my wishes known and there is no hope of recovery," or "if my family can't care for me at home and I must live in an institution."

You may want to consider some of the following conditions when you prepare your statement.

- living in a nursing home or other institution
- chronic incurable pain
- in permanent coma
- unable to feed, wash, dress, walk or talk

– blind, deaf
– not able to recognize family
– not able to communicate
– loss of control over bowel or bladder
– paralysed from the neck down

After you define what you consider an irreversible condition, you must consider what level of care you would want in that condition. You will probably want to request more care if your condition is reversible. Many people who develop a life-threatening illness want palliative care with no CPR if their condition is irreversible and they already have a serious irreversible disability, but may request more care for a reversible condition. Some examples of personal statements are included at the end of this section for your guidance.

In your personal statement try to mention any specific wishes you might have. If you don't want certain medical procedures used under any circumstances, for religious or other reasons, you should state this here. If you have any particular quirks about how you would like to be buried or cremated, use the personal statement for that purpose.

Organ Donation

In the last twenty years, since drugs have been developed to prevent the body's rejection of transplanted tissue from another human, organ donation has become widespread. Many of us know someone who is alive today only because he or she received a heart, lung, kidney, liver or bone marrow from another. Some people who once suffered from blindness can see again because of corneal transplants.

Please consider whether you would like to donate your organs to others before making your personal statement. We have included a section that can be filled out to let others know your wishes.

A section on blood transfusion has been included for Jehovah's Witnesses.

EXAMPLES OF PERSONAL STATEMENTS

Example No. 1
I would consider an irreversible condition to be any condition that leaves me permanently unable to wash, dress or feed myself. I am 79 years old, recently widowed. I have no immediate family and live in a retirement home. I am in good health at the moment, but this could change at any time.

In the event of a stroke or other illness that causes me to lose my speech, paralyses one side, or disables me to the point where I can't wash, dress or feed myself, then I would want *palliative* measures only, no tube feeding or intravenous lines. In this state I would not want to be resuscitated if I have a cardiac arrest and would just want *basic* feeding.

However, if I got sick *now* with a reversible illness, I would like one attempt made to resuscitate me if I have a cardiac arrest. Just provide mechanical pumping — no tubes or drugs. If I develop a reversible illness I would want *maximum* care, but no ICU. Give me Basic and Supplemental feeding if I have a reversible life-threatening illness and cannot eat.

Example No. 2
I would consider my condition to be irreversible if I am permanently and totally dependent on others for my personal care. I am 64 years old. I suffer from Parkinson's disease. I am presently able to drive and pilot my own plane with a co-pilot. I am well aware that as my disease progresses I will become less and less active. I can't accept being totally bedridden and totally dependent on others for personal care.

In the event of irreversible illness, I do not want my life maintained by artificial means. I would ask for no CPR and *palliative* care when this time comes. At this time give me only *supplemental Feeding* with no intravenous or tubes.

At the present time, I would want *surgical* care for a reversible condition, and I would want CPR if I have a cardiac arrest. Right now I would want special diets, intravenous fluids, and any feeding tubes that are necessary.

Example No. 3

I would consider my condition to be irreversible if I had to depend on others to wash, dress or feed me with no hope of recovery. I am a 35-year-old nurse. I have two young children. At this time if I develop any reversible illness I would want *intensive care.* If I have a cardiac arrest I would want every possible effort made to resuscitate me. At this time hold nothing back. Do blood work, IVs, x-rays and scans. Give me *supplemental feeding,* but no tube or intravenous feeding. I would accept an IV for comfort — for example, if it were given to treat dehydration.

However, if I develop any irreversible condition that disables me to the point where I cannot function independently, I would only want *palliative* measures. As long as I have my hands and I can look after myself I would accept this. I can accept paraplegia. I cannot accept quadriplegia, or a stroke that significantly affects my speech, leaves me incontinent, and requires others to wash and dress me. In this state I would not want to be resuscitated if I had a cardiac arrest. I would want a painless death — peaceful and quiet — no blood work, no IV, no x-rays, no scans and no tube feeding.

Do a post mortem, take all the organs you want, give my body to science.

Example No. 4
I would consider my condition to be irreversible if I were so short of breath that I could not walk or take care of myself and had no hope of recovery. I am a 60-year-old with chronic bronchitis. I have been in hospital three times this year already. On the last occasion I was put on a breathing machine (ventilator) because I could not breathe for myself. Now I can't walk out to pick up the mail because I get so short of breath. I am happy now but I don't want things to get much worse.

If I get sick again, give me antibiotics, aerosols, or oxygen, but please don't put me on the breathing machine again. If I can't eat, just keep up the intravenous line and give me *supplemental feeding*. I don't want any feeding tubes.

I am afraid that I would not be able to get off the breathing machine and I would be stuck on it. If I have a cardiac arrest — let me go please. I have thought about this and discussed it with my family. We all agree.

Post mortem and organ donation are fine. Take whatever organs are needed to help someone else.

Example No. 5
I would consider my condition to be irreversible if I were so short of breath or had angina so bad that I was unable to walk, dress or take care of myself. I am a 65-year-old retired executive. I loved golf and fishing. I had a heart attack four years ago and bypass surgery last year. I have angina now when I walk upstairs. I sometimes wake up short of breath.

The last time I was in hospital, I had a cardiac arrest and had to be brought back. I know that I could go at any second. I don't want any more surgery. If I go again, I would not want to be resuscitated. If I get into failure again I would want *surgical* care with special diets, but would not want to go into the intensive care unit. I would not mind a post mortem, and would be happy to give my organs to anyone who needed them. Please do not give me intravenous feeding. Do not pass any feeding tubes into my stomach if I ever become unconscious or cannot eat.

Example No. 6
I would consider my condition to be irreversible if I were permanently confined to bed or had to spend most of my time in the hospital. I am 35 years old. I have AIDS. I have been in hospital three times this year and have lost more than fifty pounds since my illness began. When I become ill again I want intravenous antibiotics, but I do not want intensive care. I do not want any intravenous or feeding tubes and do not want a breathing machine (ventilator).

If I have a cardiac arrest, please let me go. I do not want to die with people pumping my chest. Do not attempt to resuscitate me.

8

Filling Out the Directive

It is an important decision to use the Personal Health Care Directive. Take your time, think about what *you* want and follow these steps.

1. Read the document carefully. If you do not understand all the terms, read chapters 3 to 7 again, or get more information from your family doctor or another health care professional.

2. Discuss the Directive with all those concerned before deciding to use it. Talk to your doctor, your family, or close friends. But make sure the final decision is *yours*, and not the result of pressure from others. If your doctor disagrees with your decision, you may want to get a second opinion.

3. Choose at least one family member or friend who will complete the document with you. Select someone you trust to understand your wishes and respect your position in this matter. This person will become your *advocate*.

Your advocate must be competent and must be relied upon to make your views known when it is necessary. He or she must be available when needed (that is, not living in a different city or country).

Tell your advocate exactly what your wishes are, and make sure he or she understands how you feel. Take time to discuss your personal statement. Make sure he or she understands what you would consider an "irreversible" condition.

4. Go to your family doctor with your advocate. Sign the Directive, and have the doctor and advocate co-sign it. Give a copy of the completed form to your doctor and advocate. You may wish to keep a copy of the Directive in a safety deposit box or with your lawyer. Wallet-sized copies of the Directive are now available. (See back page for ordering information.)

5. Tell your family and friends that you have prepared this Directive, and who your advocate is.

6. Decide how often you would like to review this document. For example, you may decide to do this once a year, or after any illness or change in your health. This decision will depend on your age, condition of your health, and life plans.

A completed Health Care Directive is provided for your consideration.

Glossary of Terms

AIDS: Acquired Immune Deficiency Syndrome has been strongly linked to the Human Immunodeficiency Virus (HIV), which weakens the body's defence against disease. It is transmitted by the exchange of certain specific body fluids under specific circumstances, and not by casual contact. There is no known cure.

Alzheimer's Disease: A disease of the brain causing progressive memory loss. With time there is loss of ability to learn and, eventually, loss of the ability to do even simple tasks. The patient's behaviour may also change. There is no known cure.

Anesthetic: A local anesthetic "freezes" the skin by making it numb to pain. With general anesthetic, a person is temporarily "put to sleep": this is used only for major medical procedures.

Angina or angina pectoris: Chest pain due to poor blood flow to the heart. Usually comes on with exercise and goes away with rest. The pain may spread to the arms and/or neck. This

40

means that the blood supply to the heart is inadequate. If it persists, the heart muscle may be damaged and result in a heart attack.

Antibiotics: Drugs used to treat infections caused by bacteria.

Basic life support: Mouth-to-mouth resuscitation and heart massage (see CPR, below).

Biopsy: Surgical removal of tissue so that it may be examined under a microscope for evidence of disease.

Bronchoscopy: A procedure in which the physician looks through a flexible tube into the airways of the lungs, using a scope with a light on the tip.

Bypass surgery: Replacement or rerouting of blood vessels to an area of the body where the blood flow is not adequate.

Cardiac arrest: Stoppage of heartbeat.

CHF: Congestive Heart Failure, caused by failure of the heart to maintain adequate circulation of blood, resulting in weakness and shortness of breath.

Colonoscopy: A procedure in which a physician looks into the large bowel through a flexible tube known as a scope.

Cornea: The clear front surface of the eye.

Corneal transplant: Surgical replacement of a damaged cornea with a donated cornea.

COPD: Chronic Obstructive Pulmonary Disease, caused by problems in the airways leading to the lungs or in the lungs themselves. The main symptom is chronic shortness of breath.

CPR: Cardio-Pulmonary Resuscitation, the use of mouth-to-mouth breathing and heart massage to restore heartbeat.

CT: Computerized Tomography or CAT scan, use of a computer to produce, from x-ray data, a view of part of the body.

Cystic Fibrosis: An inherited disease that causes chronic lung infections and poor function of the pancreas in young people. There is no known cure, but treatment can prolong the patient's life to about thirty years of age.

Defibrillator: An instrument that shocks the heart with an electric current to revive it or to correct its rhythm.

Dehydration: Loss of water from the body.

Dialysis: A method of filtering and cleaning the blood of patients with kidney problems.

ECT: Electroconvulsive therapy, the use of an

electric shock to treat specific types of mental illness, for example, acute depression.

EEG: Electroencephalogram, a method of measuring brain activity.

EMG: Electromyogram, a method of measuring muscle and nerve function.

Endoscopy: Looking inside any body cavity by means of a scope.

External cardiac massage: Massage of the heart by applying pressure on the chest to maintain circulation.

Fibre-optic scope: An instrument used for looking inside body cavities.

Fractured hip: A break in the thigh bone (the femur) between the hip and the knee. Breaks usually occur at the upper part of the bone just below where it fits into the hip bone (the pelvis).

Gastrostomy: A surgical opening into the stomach so that a tube can be put directly into the stomach, usually for feeding.

Hepatitis: Swelling of the liver, caused by alcohol abuse, viral and bacterial infections.

Incontinence: Loss of control of bladder or bowel.

Intestine: Bowel.

Intravenous (IV): Injection of fluid into the body through a fine tube into a vein.

Investigations: Tests done by the doctor, such as blood tests, scans, x-rays, etc.

Irreversible illness: An illness that cannot be cured.

Kidney machine: The machine used in dialysis to clean the blood of people with kidney problems.

Laparotomy: Surgery to explore the abdomen, usually to find the cause of pain or blockage.

Life support: Machines used to keep a person alive by maintaining circulation and ventilation (breathing).

Life-threatening illness: Any illness that can cause death.

Nasogastric tube: Tube put down the nose and into the stomach for feeding or drainage.

Palliative care: Care that provides comfort and relief from pain, but does not aim to cure the condition.

Paraplegia: Loss of all sensation and movement in the lower half of the body.

Parkinson's Disease: A disorder of part of the

brain, causes a tremor ("shakes") when at rest, difficulty rising from chairs and a slow, shuffling walk. Although not curable, symptoms can be improved with medication.

Personal statement: Section in the "Let Me Decide" Directive where people state what level of irreversible disability they consider unacceptable, and express their wishes regarding post mortem, organ donation, blood transfusion, and cremation or burial.

Pneumonia: Infection and congestion of the lungs.

Post mortem: Autopsy, usually to find the cause of death.

Pulmonary embolism: Blood clot in the lung that often arises or breaks off from a clot in the calves.

Quadriplegia: Loss of all sensation and movement below the neck.

Resuscitate: To restore life by giving mouth-to-mouth breathing and/or heart massage.

Reversible illness: An illness that *can* be cured.

Scans: A method of looking inside the body without surgery. Can involve the injection of a dye that can be seen by a special x-ray.

SLE: Systemic Lupus Erythematosus, chronic disease that affects many organs, joints and skin. It is caused when the body's defence mechanism turns on itself. The course of the disease varies greatly from person to person; however, it is not curable. Known as Lupus.

Special diet: Diet geared to the specific nutritional needs of patients, such as diabetics.

Stroke: Sudden damage to the brain caused by lack of oxygen, often resulting in weakness, slurred speech, loss of movement, etc. These losses may or may not improve over time.

Terminal illness: Illness from which a person will not recover and will eventually die.

TIA: Transient Ischemic Attack, temporary block of the blood supply to the brain, causing weakness, slurred speech, loss of movement and memory lapses, lasting from a few moments to several hours.

Total parenteral nutrition: Complete nutrition (proteins, sugars, fats, vitamins and minerals) given by injection through a vein.

Transplant: An organ or tissue taken from the body for use in another area of the same body or for use in another person's body.

Ventilator: Breathing machine or respirator.

III. PERSONAL HEALTH CARE CHART

This chart is to be consulted only if I am no longer able to make or communicate my own decisions.
My choices are noted in the spaces provided below each section.

	In the event of Life-Threatening Illness, please provide the following care: ↓		In the event I am not able to feed myself, please provide the following care: ↓		In the event of Cardiac Arrest, please provide the following care: ↓	
	If my condition is:		If my condition is:		If my condition is:	
	REVERSIBLE ↓	IRREVERSIBLE ↓	REVERSIBLE ↓	IRREVERSIBLE ↓	REVERSIBLE ↓	IRREVERSIBLE ↓
	Palliative / Limited / Surgical / Intensive	Palliative / Limited / Surgical / Intensive	Basic / Supplemental / Intravenous / Tube	Basic / Supplemental / Intravenous / Tube	No CPR / CPR	No CPR / CPR
Write your choice here	Intensive	Palliative	Tube	Basic	CPR	No CPR
Date and initial here	Date: 2/20/92	Patient: *[signature]*	Advocate #1: *[signature]*	Advocate #2: *jr.*	Physician: *[signature]*	

This document should be reviewed once a year, after an illness, or if there is any change in health.

You can use the space below to show any changes in your Directive.

Write your choice here						
Date and initial here	Date:	Patient:	Advocate #1:	Advocate #2:	Physician:	
Write your choice here						
Date and initial here	Date:	Patient:	Advocate #1:	Advocate #2:	Physician:	

Copyright © Dr D.W. Molloy

DR WILLIAM MOLLOY

*Cordially invites you
to learn further about*

LET ME DECIDE

through other available material including:

VIDEO: My Health Care — I Decide

This 20-minute video explores the need for, and the role of advance health care directives in empowering individuals to take control of their health care. It contains interviews with health care providers, patients, and families in various settings: wards in community hospitals, the community, hospital family conferences and nursing homes.

Price $30(Can), $25(U.S.)

Please send me _____ copies.

AUDIO: LET ME DECIDE Tapes

Cassette tapes are available for those who are unable to read or who would prefer to learn by listening.

Price $12(Can), $10(U.S.)

Please send me _____ copies.

TRANSLATIONS of LET ME DECIDE

Let Me Decide is available in other languages.

Price $5(Cdn)

Systematic programs have been developed to educate health care professionals, community organizations, institutional staff, patients and families about the Directive. These educational programs contain background material on directives, the video "My Health Care — I Decide," slide presentations, copies of the Directive and information on how to implement the directive in various settings. Bulk orders of the "Let Me Decide" Directive are available for organizations and institutions. Wallet-sized health care charts are also available.

To order the above material or receive additional information, please write:

LET ME DECIDE
673 UPPER JAMES STREET
P.O. BOX 60615
HAMILTON, ONTARIO
CANADA L9C 7N7

LET ME DECIDE
615 MAIN STREET
M.P.O. BOX 2487
NIAGARA FALLS, NEW YORK
U.S.A. 14302

or call:
1-900-567-3300

Send Canadian or U.S. cheque or money order only. Allow up to six weeks for delivery. *To avoid any delay in receiving your order, be sure to enclose the following:*

1. Your cheque or money order made payable to "Let Me Decide."
2. Clearly printed full name, phone number, street, city, province or state, postal or zip code.

PLEASE DO NOT SEND CASH THROUGH THE MAIL